The Missing Piece

Tana Reiff

A Pacemaker **LifeTimes™ 2** Book

The Missing Piece

Tana Reiff
AR B.L.: 2.7
Points: 0.5   UG

LifeTimes™ 2 Titles

Take Away Three
Climbing the Wall
The Door Is Open
Just for Today
Chicken by Che
Play Money
The Missing Piece

Cover illustration: Terry Hoff

Library of Congress Catalog Card Number: 87-80040

ISBN 0-8224-4608-1

Printed in the United States of America

7 8 9 10 11 12   07 06 05 04 03

Globe Fearon
Pearson Learning Group

1-800-321-3106
www.pearsonlearning.com

Contents

CHAPTER 1

"Could you bring me
a glass of water?"
the woman asked.
She was sitting
at table six.

"I'll be with you
in a minute,"
called Julie.

It was a busy night
at the restaurant.
Julie was doing
the best she could.
Only she and Phong
were working.
They were waiting on
nine tables each.

But Julie's mind
was not on the people

or the food.
Her mind
was on Bill.
Tonight she would be
with wonderful Bill.
Beautiful, wonderful Bill.
He played drums
in a rock band.
He was all
Julie could think about.

Julie would get off work
at 4:00.
She would rush home.
She would cook Bill
a dinner
he would never forget.

Was there enough room
on the stove?
She would
cook the potatoes first.
Then she could put
the chicken
in the oven.

That would leave
enough room
on top of the stove.

"Someone over there
wants you,"
said Julie's friend, Phong.

"Where is
my glass of water, miss?"
called the woman
at table six.

Julie broke out
of her dream.
She had forgotten
where she was.
"Coming right up!"
she called back
to the woman.

Maybe Bill will stay
for breakfast,
Julie said to herself.
And maybe someday

he'll marry me.
My sister had
a beautiful wedding
last year.
Maybe soon
I'll have
a beautiful wedding, too.

Julie went to get
the glass of water.
When she got back,
the woman was gone.
She had left
no tip for Julie.

Thinking It Over

1. Do you ever have
    a hard time
    keeping your mind
    on your work?
    Why?

2. What do you daydream about?

3. Do you think
    Julie thinks too much
    about Bill?

CHAPTER 2

Bill was late
for Julie's big dinner.
Finally, he showed up.

"I'm sorry,"
he said.
"We had
a little problem
with the band."

"It's OK,"
Julie told him.
"I love you anyway."

Bill said nothing
in return.

They sat down
to eat dinner.
"Bill," said Julie.

"I really want
to get married."

Bill stopped eating.
"What are you
talking about?"
he asked.
"You and I
have only known each other
for two months!"

Julie grabbed
Bill's hand.
"But I want
to be with you,"
she begged.
"I would do anything
for you."

"It's a bit early
to talk about
getting married,"
said Bill.
"Don't you think?"

"We could live together,"
said Julie.
"Why don't you move in?"

Bill stopped to think
for a minute.
He did need
a place to stay.

"OK," he said.
"I'll move in."

Julie got up
and danced
around the floor.
"This is wonderful!
Just wonderful!"
she cried.

Bill went back
to his dinner.
"This chicken
isn't bad,"
he said.

Thinking It Over

1.   Why did Bill say nothing
      when Julie said
      she loves him?

2.   What would you have done here
      if you were Bill?

3.   Do you think
      people should live together
      without being married?

CHAPTER 3

The next day
at break time
Julie told Phong
about Bill.
"He's going to move in!"
Julie said.

Phong was from
the Far East.
She had come
to this country
during the war.
She had seen
some bad times.

"What's Bill like?"
Phong asked.
"What's so great
about this man?"

"He plays
in a rock band,"

Julie told her.
"And someday soon
he's going to marry me."

"What's so great
about that?"
asked Phong.
"Will he help
around the house?
Will he help
pay the bills?"

"I don't know,"
said Julie.
"We'll talk about all that
when the time comes.
When we're married,
everything will be just right."

"Why are you
in such a rush?"
asked Phong.
"Do you think getting married
is the answer to everything?
It won't give you
everything you want."

Julie didn't seem to hear
what Phong was saying.
She was looking
at a magazine for brides.
"Look at this dress!"
she cried.
"Isn't it beautiful?"

Phong didn't seem to care.
"You'll come back
from your wedding trip
and life will go on,"
she said.
"You'll still be you.
Bill will still be Bill.
Getting married
won't make either of you
any better."

"But," said Julie,
"I'll be with Bill.
That's all
that matters!"

Thinking It Over

1. Why do you think
    Phong is saying these things
    about marriage?

2. What do you think
    getting married
    does to people?

CHAPTER 4

Bill's band was playing
at the club
Saturday night.
Julie went along
to hear the band
and see Bill play.

Between sets
Bill came over
and sat with Julie.

"When are we
going to get married?"
she whispered in his ear.

"We don't have to talk
about that now,"
said Bill.
"I just moved in
with you.

Besides, we don't have
enough money.
This band isn't bad.
But we're not going to sell
a big record
anytime soon."

   "I have an idea,"
said Julie.
"I'll get a night job.
Then we'll have
enough money."

   Bill wasn't so sure
it was a good idea.
"I've seen
too many friends
get married,"
he said.
"At least half of them
aren't married anymore.
And it didn't take long."

   The lead singer
called for Bill.

It was time
to play the next set.
"I have to go,"
said Bill.
"Wish me luck.
I do a great bit
in the next song."

"Good luck,"
said Julie.
"I'll just go back
to my drink."

Thinking It Over

1. Do you think money
    is the real reason
    Bill doesn't want
    to get married now?

2. Do you think Julie
    pushes too much?

3. What do you do
    when a friend
    wants to talk about something,
    and you don't?

CHAPTER 5

Julie got
a night job anyway.
She worked at an all-night
self-service gas station.
She took the money
and gave people their change.

She couldn't see Bill
most nights anyway.
He was out playing
in the band.
That was OK.
Making money
was most important now.
The more money
she could make,
the sooner she and Bill
could get married.
She could see Bill
late at night
when she got home.

One night
when Julie got home,
Bill was already there.
He and two guys
from the band
were watching TV.
They were drinking.
The TV was loud.
So were the guys.

"Why are you home
so early?"
Julie asked.

"It's a long story,"
said Bill.
"But the bottom line is,
the band broke up.
We can't work together
any longer.
We're finished."

"Oh, no!"
cried Julie.
Her heart began to sink.

She didn't care much
about the band.
All she could think about
was the money.
"Now it will take even longer
before we can get married,"
she said.

The guys laughed.
"We didn't know
you were getting married,"
they said.
"Why didn't you tell us
the good news?"

Bill didn't answer.
He just laughed along
with them.

Thinking It Over

1. Why do you think
    Bill didn't tell his friends
    he was getting married?

2. Did you ever get so busy
    with something
    that you forgot
    why you were doing it?

3. Do you think Bill
    is getting more than he gives?

CHAPTER 6

Weeks went by.
Bill couldn't find
a new band
to play in.
He and the two guys
from the old band
couldn't find anyone
to make a new band.

Instead, Bill and the guys
hung out at Julie's place
all the time.
Night after night
they got six-packs
of beer.
They had fun,
but they made a mess.
Julie gave Bill
the money for the beer.

Julie kept her job
at the gas station.
Every night
she came home
to find a party.
Her night job
just about paid
for Bill's parties.

"Someone called for you,"
said Bill one night.
"I wrote down the number
in the kitchen."

When Julie saw the number
she almost fell over.
It was her mother's number.
She called right away.

"Who answered the phone?"
asked Julie's mother.

"That was Bill,"
said Julie.

"He's a good friend
 of mine."

"He doesn't live there,
does he?"
asked her mother.

"No, no,"
said Julie.
"But he's here often.
In fact,
I want to tell you
the good news.
We're getting married.
We'll be married
in about three months."

Julie's mother
was very happy.
"So you found yourself
a husband!"
she said.
"I'm going to throw you
a big party."

"Don't do that,"
said Julie.

"I want to, dear,"
said her mother.
"You don't have to do
a thing.
Just be there, OK?
And Julie, dear,
I can't wait
to meet your young man."

Thinking It Over

1.   How is Julie
     getting herself into trouble?
     What should she
     have told her mother?

2.   Do you think Bill
     is lazy?

3.   How is Julie's mother
     pushing her to get married?

CHAPTER 7

Julie's mother
made plans
for the party
for Julie and Bill.
She sent cards
to all her friends.
The party would be
held at a big hall.
It was a month away.
Julie didn't tell Bill.
He didn't know
a thing about the party.

If Julie was home,
she always answered the phone.
She didn't want her mother
to talk to Bill.
But Julie was often
away from home.
She was working
60 hours a week.

One night
Julie's mother called,
and Bill answered.
"Are you all ready
for the big party?"
she said.

"What big party?"
asked Bill.

"The big party
I'm throwing
for you and Julie,"
said Julie's mother.
"I can't wait
to see the ring
you gave my little girl.

When Julie got home
Bill was very angry.
He told her
about her mother's call.
"What is going on?"
he asked.

Julie began to cry.
"I'm sorry, Bill,"
said Julie.
"I told my mother
we were getting married.
She wants to have
a big party.
It wasn't my idea!"

"But you didn't stop her,
did you?"
asked Bill.
"Why not?"

"I just want
to marry you,"
said Julie.
"I'm tired of waiting.
You said
we could get married
when we had
enough money.
I've been working and working.
You have parties

every night.
Parties that I pay for.
It's not fair."

"Did I ever
come out and say
I want to get married?"
asked Bill.

"Not really,"
said Julie.

"Maybe you're right
about the parties,"
said Bill.
"But I never lied to you
about getting married.
You're the one
who wants to get married."

"I'm really sorry,"
said Julie.

"Your mother's party
is a big joke,"

said Bill.
"My living here
is a big joke, too.
You have your mind
on only one thing.
And I can't take it.
You have a problem,
you know it?
But this is it.
I'm leaving."

"Where will you go?"
asked Julie.

"I don't know,"
said Bill.
He stormed out.
It was the last time
Julie ever saw him.

Thinking It Over

1. Do you think Bill
   has a right to be angry?

2. How did Bill and Julie
   lie to each other?

3. How do people get themselves
   into such trouble?

CHAPTER 8

"Oh, Phong,"
cried Julie.
"What have I done?"

Julie told Phong
the whole story.
"This thing with Bill
was all a big lie,"
Julie said.
"He never wanted
to marry me.
I let things
get out of hand.
Now I have to tell my mother
that Bill is gone.
What am I going to do?"

"You're going
to tell your mother
that Bill is gone!"
said Phong.
"It's that simple."

"Oh, Phong,
what's wrong with me?"
Julie asked her friend.

"You want to be happy
like everyone else,"
said Phong.
"But maybe you are looking
in the wrong places.
To be happy,
you must be happy
with yourself.
You can't look
to someone else
to make you happy.

Then Phong told
her own story.
"I wanted
to get married once,"
she said.
"I wanted to come
to this country
very, very much.
I could see
only one way

to do it.
I had to marry
an American man.
So I did.
He brought me
to this country.
And I got
my green card.

　"But that man
turned out to be mean.
He beat me, Julie.
He took my money.
After a while,
I had to get out.
So the marriage broke up.
Getting married
got me to this country.
But it did not
make me happy."

　"You seem happy now,"
said Julie.

　"I'm pretty happy,"
said Phong.

"But that's because
I looked inside myself.
I learned
to make it on my own.
I live
in a free country.
Here it is possible
to make it on my own.
I make good money.
I take care
of myself.
I feel very good
about that.
That is what
makes me happy.
You must look
inside yourself, too, Julie."

"You are a good friend,"
said Julie.
"You are a good teacher.
I'll work on
what you told me.
And someday
I'll give you something
in return."

Thinking It Over

1. Do you believe
    the only way to be happy
    is to be happy
    with yourself?

2. Do you believe
    getting married
    can make you happy?

3. What's the smartest thing
    anyone ever told you?

CHAPTER 9

Julie missed Bill.
But she remembered
what Phong had told her.
She was glad
to have jobs
at the gas station
and the restaurant.
She was happy with herself
for doing well
on both jobs.

Then the boss
at the gas station
made her feel even better.
"You are the best worker
I have ever had,"
he said.
"I would like you
to work here full-time.
Would you like
a full-time day job?"

"I'll think about it,"
said Julie.
"I would have to give up
my other job."

"You can make more money here
than at your other job,"
said the boss.
"I think
you should work here full-time."

With Bill gone,
Julie didn't need two jobs.
So she left
the restaurant job.
She hated to leave Phong.
But the new job
was too good to pass up.
Phong would understand
her reasons.

Julie liked full-time work
at the gas station.
The hours were good.
The money was good.
She liked the deal.

Besides, this was
a big company.
There were places to go
in this company.

Now Julie had
nothing to do
at night.
She signed up
for a business course
at the adult school.
If there were places to go
in this company,
then she might as well
learn how
to go there.

Julie also worked overtime
without more pay.
She didn't mind.

"You're doing great,"
said the boss.
"I wish all my workers
were like you."

Thinking It Over

1. Would you have stayed
    at the restaurant
    or gone to work full-time
    at the gas station?
    Why?

2. In what ways
    is Julie doing
    what Phong said
    she should do?

3. How can you tell
    Julie is feeling good
    about herself?

CHAPTER 10

A few months later
the boss called Julie
into his office.
"The company is sending me
to a bigger station,"
he said.
"I'm going to ask them
to give you
my job here."

"You're kidding!"
cried Julie.

"No, I'm not,"
said the boss.
"I think
they'll give you the job
if you want it.
What should I tell them?"

"Tell them
I'm interested,"
said Julie.
"And don't forget
to tell them
I've been taking
a business course!"

A few weeks after that
the boss called Julie
into his office again.
"The company wants
to talk to you.
Can you go
to the main office
at 10:00 Tuesday morning?"

"I'll be there,"
said Julie.

On Tuesday morning
Julie met with a group
of people
at the main office.

Their talk went well.
Julie said
all the right things.

A few days later
she got a letter
from the main office.
The boss's job
was hers!

Julie called Phong.
"I got the job!"
she told Phong.
"Let's go out and party!"

"Now you're talking!"
said Phong.
"I'm so happy for you!"

Thinking It Over

1. Why is Julie's work
    going so well?

2. Why did the company
    give Julie the boss's job?

3. When does school or work
    go best for you?

CHAPTER 11

Being the boss
was not easy.
Julie had to tell
the other workers
what to do.
She had to take care
of money matters.
She had to do
a lot of paperwork.
She worked
long hours.
But it was worth it.
She made better money.
And she felt good
about what she could do.

Julie also had to go
to meetings
at the main office.
She was afraid
to go to the first meeting.

There were only three women.
There were ten men.

A nice-looking man
was sitting across the table.
He kept looking at Julie
during the meeting.
She looked at him, too.

After the meeting,
he came over
to talk to her.
"My name is Mike,"
he said.
"Where is your station?"
he asked.

"Right off the main road,"
explained Julie.
"You'll have to stop in
and see it sometime.
I keep it looking good."

Mike smiled.
"I'd like to

do that," he said.
"How about if I
come by right before
you get off?
Would you go out
with me
after work?"

"OK, it's a date,"
Julie said.

So Julie and Mike
went out Friday night
after work.
They went to dinner
and a movie.
Then they went back
to Julie's place.

"I'm having a nice time,"
said Mike.
"Are you?"

"Yes, Mike,"
said Julie.
"You're fun."

"May I stay overnight?"
Mike asked.

Julie was just about
to say yes.
But she stopped herself.
"We just met,"
she said.
"Let's not
rush things.
But I'd like to see you again."

"Sorry," said Mike.
"I didn't mean
to move too fast."

"It's OK,"
said Julie.
"Let's just give it time."

Thinking It Over

1. How can you tell
    Julie is changing?

2. Where are the best places
    to meet new people?

3. Should men and woman
    who work for
    the same company
    go out together?

CHAPTER 12

Julie and Mike
spent more and more time together.
They enjoyed
each other's company.
But no one
was in a rush
to get married.

They both
had to work
a lot of hours, too.
They couldn't see each other
whenever they wanted to.
Sometimes work came first.

One night
Mike called Julie
at her gas station.
"I have a little problem,"
he said.
"I have a new young man

working at my station.
His name is Dao.
He's a great worker.
He's from the Far East.
He's always asking me
if I know any women
he could go out with.
I really don't
know anyone."

"I don't believe
you're telling me this,"
said Julie.
"I happen to have
a friend from the Far East.
Her name is Phong.
She might want
to go out with Dao."

"Will you ask her?"
said Mike.

"Sure," said Julie.
"And you're sure
this Dao is a nice guy?"

    "Oh, yes,"
said Mike.
"I like him a lot.
I just wish
he could find a woman!"

    Julie couldn't wait
to talk to Phong.
She hoped
that Phong
would want to go out with Dao.
Maybe this was the way
Julie could give Phong
something in return
for her help.

Thinking It Over

1.   Would you turn down
     a good time
     for your job?

2.   Why do you think
     Dao is having a hard time
     finding a woman?

3.   Do you think friends
     should "set up" friends
     to go out with each other?

CHAPTER 13

Phong was happy
to meet Dao.
It was hard for her
to meet men
from the Far East.

Julie and Mike
and Phong and Dao
all went out together.
They went out to eat
at a Far Eastern restaurant.

"This food doesn't taste
like they make it
back home,"
laughed Phong.

Dao laughed, too.
"You should taste
the food I cook,"

he said.
"Now *that* is good."

"I think the food
tastes good."
said Mike.

"So do I,"
said Julie.
"It's a bit strange,
but I like it."

"It's not bad,"
said Dao.
"It's just different!
But you might as well
learn to eat it right."

Dao and Phong
showed Julie and Mike
how to eat
with chopsticks.
Julie and Mike
kept dropping food
back to their plates.

Dao and Phong
had no problem.
They ate everything fast.

"I have some news,"
said Julie.
"I wanted to tell you
all together.
I got a call
from the main office.
I am getting
another new job.
I will be taking care
of five gas stations!"

Everyone was happy
for Julie.

But when Mike
took her home,
he asked her a question.
"Will your new job
mean we'll see even less
of each other?"
he asked.

      "I hope not,"
said Julie.
"You and the job
both mean a lot to me."

      "I love you, Julie,"
said Mike.
He took her
in his arms.
"I might want
to marry you someday."

      "I might want
to marry you, too,"
said Julie.
She looked him
in the eyes.
"Not so long ago
I believed
that getting married
would make me happy.
Now I know
it takes more than that.
There was something missing
in my life.

And it wasn't a husband.
The missing piece
was inside me,
just like Phong said."

  "You should be very happy,"
said Mike.
"You have done
very well for yourself."

  "I *am* happy,"
said Julie.
"And if I end up married,
maybe I'll be even happier."

  "So many people
want only to get married,"
said Mike.
"I'm glad
you're looking for more."

  "Why don't you come in?"
Julie asked Mike.
"I'd like you
to sit with me for a while."

Thinking It Over

1.   Why are Julie and Mike
     better off than Julie and Bill?

2.   What was Julie's missing piece?

3.   What makes you happy?